PROJECT RISE

@COLLINHENDERSON

COLLIN HENDERSON

WWW.THECOLLINHENDERSON.COM

RISE JOURNAL

A SIMPLE YET POWERFUL SYSTEM TO HELP YOU BE THE BEST VERSION OF YOU EACH DAY.

THIS RISE JOURNAL BELONGS TO:

Petra

RISE

Verb
1. move from a lower position to a higher one; go or come up
2. get up from lying, sitting, or kneeling

Noun
1. an upward movement; an instance of becoming higher
2. an increase in amount, extent, size, or number

THE TIME IS NOW

How are you feeling right now? Stressed? Excited? Nervous? Confident? Hopeful? Regardless if you are crushing it or feeling crushed...just know this: you don't need to be hurting to get help or to help yourself.

The time is NOW to take the necessary steps to RISE and become the best version of you. LET'S GO!!!

Several years ago, I hit a low point personally and professionally and used a specific set of daily rituals to get me out of a funk and onto a path to maximize my potential. This is my best practice. This is my most precious gift that I can give away—the tools to help you RISE.

Based on my research in positive psychology and personal experiences related to success and achievement, I have developed a simple daily journaling format to help create clarity for attacking each day with purpose and passion. This system will improve your mindset, help you craft a plan for success, and give you the motivation to act. Maximizing your personal development is all about taking ACTION. Improving yourself will not happen by sitting on your butt. You can't just snap your fingers and expect to get better. Make the most important decision you can make RIGHT NOW, and invest in your well-being. You'll thank yourself months and years from now. In the end, successful people do what others are not willing to do.

This system only takes about five to ten minutes each day. That is it! The best life coach and business strategist in the world, Tony Robbins, says, "If you don't have ten minutes, you don't have a life." That means you! You owe it to yourself and the people you love to invest in your mind, body, and spirit—not just occasionally—but daily. Let this journal be your guide. When you have the proper mindset, there is nothing you can't accomplish.

Here's the formula to RISE:

1. MASTER THE ART OF GOAL SETTING AND ATTAINMENT.
The power of goal setting is time tested. I provide a simple framework that creates vision and purpose for your near and distant future.

2. CREATE A SYSTEM OF WRITING DOWN YOUR THOUGHTS, INTENTIONS, AND GOALS (HENCE THE RISE JOURNAL).

It is scientifically proven that writing your thoughts, feelings, and goals down create better results than not writing them down. This approach will give you clarity and create a road map to be your best self.

3. PRACTICE GRATITUDE.

The foundation of being your best self starts with being grateful. Focusing on what you have instead of what you don't have is the first step to attracting more good in your life.

4. IDENTIFY YOUR ONE KEY OBJECTIVE FOR THE DAY.

Many people get distracted by tasks that don't even matter. Isolating one clear objective daily will help you win the day and gain the necessary momentum of achieving what you want.

5. GIVE YOURSELF DAILY AFFIRMATIONS.

What you say to yourself is ten times more powerful than what anybody else can say to you. Take control of your inner-voice, and let go of negative thought patterns. The single act of taking control of your self-talk is one of the most crucial habits to becoming your best self.

6. LEARN SOMETHING NEW EVERYDAY.

The concept of learning can be found in two forms: 1) Failing forward and learning from your mistakes; and 2) Making a conscious effort to invest in your personal development by reading, listening, watching educational information, or learning new information from mentors. Learning and growing will take you to ultimate fulfillment.

7. SERVE OTHERS.

You don't start living, until you start giving. Living a life with a servant leader mindset creates less stress, better health, more influence, and wealth—wealth in relationships and prosperity.

8. VISUALIZE YOUR GOALS AND ACTION STEPS DAILY, AS IF YOU HAVE ALREADY ACCOMPLISHED THEM.

Your brain is a magnet. Visualizing your action and outcome goals as if you already have them creates a pathway for your body and soul to follow. Thoughts become things. When you establish the habit of filtering your mind to focus on positive outcomes instead of negative, you will take control of your life and attract abundance and success.

Before you get started, there are a few questions you must address in order to improve your mindset.

What do you want? Don't worry about what others might think or what you might assume you are expected to say. Just be as honest as possible. Clarity is power. In the space below, capture in words what your heart desires.

WHAT DO YOU WANT?

_____

_____

_____

Can you identify a roadblock that is keeping you from achieving greatness? Is it your own thoughts, a person, an obstacle, past failures, guilt or shame? Just by identifying this adversity, you can create a plan to overcome it.

Answer this question: **WHAT IS HOLDING ME BACK RIGHT NOW FROM GETTING WHAT I WANT?**

_____

_____

_____

THE PERSON I WILL TALK TO ABOUT MY FEAR (OR WHAT IS HOLDING ME BACK) IS:

_____

I WILL TALK TO THIS PERSON BY THIS DATE:

_____

Can you identify a common negative thought that you may be consistently telling yourself (ex: I'm a horrible public speaker – that used to mine; I'm under qualified; I'm too small; I'm too young; I'm too old; I'm not talented enough; they don't like me). **IDENTIFY THAT THOUGHT HERE:**

_____

_____

Know that it is perfectly normal to have negative thoughts pop into your head. The human brain is millions of years old. It's designed to survive by avoiding pain, failure, and embarrassment. It is not designed to thrive. The secret is to filter negative thoughts, and create a mental habit and system to limit these mental patterns. One method is to recognize that this internal judge is a liar, a fraud, and a fake—this voice is not your true self. Every person on the planet has automatic negative thoughts (some more than others). Successful people are able to limit these thoughts and keep their mind on track.

An approach to combat these automatic negative thoughts is to create a special word or phrase that you say to yourself when you recognize your internal judge pop-up. This special word or phrase is sometimes called your mantra, motto, slogan, or catchphrase. For example, Nike's slogan is "Just Do It." This word or phrase will help you snap your mind away from negativity and into a more positive state.

THE MOTTO THAT I WILL USE TO IMPROVE MY MINDSET, QUIET MY NEGATIVE THOUGHT(S), AND TAKE ACTION IS:

_____

_____

VISION PT. 1

THE PERFECT DAY

Having a clear vision in your life is so powerful.
Take a moment and visualize what a perfect day would look like for
you. What time are you waking up? Where will you be? What are
you doing? Who are you with? This exercise is a simple first step to
begin with the end in mind. Make a list and describe in as much
detail as you can—living a day in the life as your best self,
doing what you love to do, with the people you care about the most.

VISION PT. 2

SEE YOUR GOAL

Writing down and even drawing your goal will help create a clear picture of what you want to achieve. Saying, hearing, and feeling something is one thing, but SEEING your goal is even more powerful. Do your best to create an image of the single moment of achieving your ultimate goal. The more visual detail you include the better.

SEE IT. BELIEVE IT. ACHIEVE IT.

Create a picture of you achieving your goal here:

RISE PLAN

Now that you have created a vision for what you want, it's time to create a plan to make it happen. Your Rise Plan is all about the Big 5 of Goal Setting, which I call G5. The reason why I call it the G5 is because it resembles a private G5 jet—it will take you wherever it is you want to go.

THE BIG 5 OF GOAL SETTING (G5):
1. Have a GOAL
2. Put it to PAPER
3. Have an ACTION plan
4. Have reasons WHY
5. Upgrade your HABITS

Take a moment and envision a jet or an airplane. Each of the five elements of successful goal setting (G5) represents a different part of the aircraft.

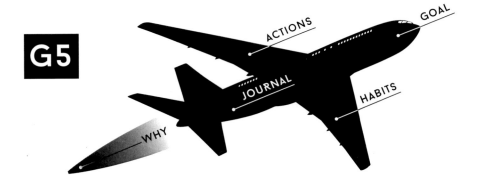

• The front of the jet represents your GOAL and where you are headed; it gives you a clear destination and direction of where you want to go.
• The two wings represent your ACTIONS and HABITS, which gives you lift and elevates you to your desired achievement.
• The jet propulsion or back of the plane represents your WHY; it gives you power and pushes you forward; it's the fuel and energy that makes you go.
• The body of the jet represents your JOURNAL and the power of putting your goal and plan on paper; it will carry you to your destination.

Now let's build your plan.

GOALS

WRITE DOWN YOUR GOALS IN THESE THREE
DIFFERENT TIME PERIODS

1 MONTH:

_____

_____

6 MONTHS TO 1 YEAR: Spanish

_____

_____

_____

_____

3 TO 10 YEARS:

_____

_____

_____

_____

ACTIONS

WRITE DOWN WHAT ACTIONS YOU MUST TAKE
IN ORDER TO ACHIEVE YOUR GOAL(S).
ALSO, FOR EACH ACTION, WRITE DOWN HOW
FREQUENT OR WHEN YOU PLAN ON MAKING
IT HAPPEN. HERE ARE THE THREE STEPS TO
CREATE YOUR ACTION PLAN:

Step 1: List your actions.
Step 2: Rank them in numeric fashion in the order you will complete them.
Step 3: Hold yourself accountable. On the far right column, add how frequent
or by what date you will achieve each action.

ACTIONS   FREQUENCY/DATE

_____   _____

_____   _____

_____   _____

_____   _____

_____   _____

_____   _____

_____   _____

ACTIONS

FREQUENCY/DATE

_____   _____

_____   _____

_____   _____

_____   _____

_____   _____

_____   _____

_____   _____

_____   _____

_____   _____

_____   _____

_____   _____

_____   _____

_____   _____

_____   _____

_____   _____

WHAT'S YOUR WHY?

MOTIVES MATTER. IT IS CRUCIAL TO IDENTIFY THE WHY BEHIND YOUR GOALS. HOW WILL YOU FEEL WHEN YOU COMPLETE YOUR MISSION? WHAT WILL ACHIEVING YOUR GOALS DO FOR YOU AND YOUR LOVED ONES? USE THE SPACE BELOW TO LIST THE REASONS BEHIND WHAT YOU WANT TO ACHIEVE.

_____

_____

_____

_____

_____

_____

_____

_____

_____

A RISING TIDE LIFTS ALL BOATS

JOHN F. KENNEDY

HABITS

ARISTOTLE ONCE SAID, *"WE ARE WHAT WE REPEATEDLY DO. EXCELLENCE IS NOT AN ACT, BUT A HABIT."* IN ORDER TO MAKE YOUR DREAM COME TO LIFE, YOU MUST TAKE OWNERSHIP OF YOUR HABITS. HERE ARE A FEW QUESTIONS TO HELP YOU STICK TO YOUR PLAN.

ACCOUNTABILITY

The person I will ask to help hold me accountable will be (here's a thought: ask this person to do the Rise Journal with you):

_____

If I give up on my plan, I promise to donate $ _____ to this charity:

_____

And/or if I give up on my plan, I promise to reprimand myself by:

_____

If I complete 30 days of journaling, I will reward myself with:

_____

The person who has what I want, that I'll ask to be my mentor is:

_____

I will ask this person to be my mentor by this date: _____

KEYSTONE HABITS

A keystone habit is one ritual that sparks a chain reaction for other good habits to follow. For example, if I exercise four days a week, I tend to eat healthier, drink more water, get more sleep, and have more energy.

By this date: _____ , I will discontinue this one bad habit:

_____

By this date: _____ , I will replace that one bad habit,
with this new keystone habit:

_____

COMMITMENTS

Goals are great, but commitments are better. We have 100% control over what we commit to do. We do not have 100% control over when and to what extent we achieve our goals (here's a hint: if you stick to your commitments consistently, you will undoubtedly achieve your goal!). Now that you have already written down your action plan, list your top three actions that you COMMIT to do consistently (include a frequency as well). Execute on your commitments, and you will RISE!

TOP 3 COMMITMENTS   FREQUENCY

_____   _____

_____   _____

_____   _____

HOW TO USE YOUR RISE JOURNAL DAILY

The application of the Rise Journal is found in the acronym **G.O.A.L.S. V.**

G – GRATITUDE
O – OBJECTIVE
A – AFFIRMATION
L – LEARN
S – SERVICE

V – VISUALIZE

Reflecting upon my life, my extensive study in positive psychology, and what brings about success and happiness, I have found that it can be summed up in these six areas:

1. Feeling **GRATITUDE** in all things…What are you grateful for today?

2. Having a clear **OBJECTIVE** each day…What's the one thing you must do to win the day?

3. Owning your self-talk with positivity through daily **AFFIRMATIONS**… Give yourself daily statements of affirmation (i.e. "I got this!" "I'm the best." I can't be stopped" "I'm worthy."). Start each day by finishing this sentence: "I am…"

4. Investing in your personal development and being intentional in **LEARNING** something new each day is one of the most powerful strategies for growth… What do you want to learn more about today? How can you learn from where you failed?

5. Being generous and **SERVING** others has been proven to reduce stress, lengthen life, and create what is called a "helpers high"…What can you do to intentionally serve and help someone today?

6. **VISUALIZING** your goals as if you already have them will create neuropathways to success…write your goals down in present tense. Picture those tasks in vivid detail as if you have already achieved them.

All of these steps done together should not take more than about five to ten minutes each day. Seriously, that's it! Just five to ten minutes. All athletes warm up their bodies before competition. Singers warm up their voice before they perform. Race car drivers warm up their engines before each race. You can't bake a pie or a pizza without preheating the oven. In order to get the change and focus you are looking for, you too need to warm up and PRIME your mindset before you begin each day.

You can work on your Rise Journal before you go to sleep at night, before you get up in the morning, or a combination of both (half in the morning and half before you go to bed)...it really doesn't matter. See my examples on the next pages.

Now it's your turn to make journaling a keystone habit that creates the clarity needed to perform at your best. Writing your thoughts, intentions, and feelings down have been scientifically proven to reduce stress, improve happiness, and increase the likelihood of achieving your goals. Good luck...I know you can do it!

Just know that there is going to be some adversity and hardships along the way. That is ok. Failing and being challenged is the only way we learn and get better. Stick to your process (journaling) and believe in this one simple statement:

THE BEST IS YET TO COME!

FOR MORE UPLIFTING CONTENT, BLOG POSTS, & VIDEOS, VISIT THECOLLINHENDERSON.COM.

G I am so grateful that I get to take my son Baylor to preschool today and pick him up as well. I love seeing that smile on his face.

O Finish my expense report and turn it in my 5pm.

A I have everything I need to finish the year #1. I've put in the work and I'm off to a great start. I'm deserving of being a champion!

L I can't wait to listen to more of the Little Red Book of Selling today in my car. I learned a key tactic yesterday on the power of using visuals to enhance the buying experience.

S I'm going to bring home flowers today for Kendra. I know this will make her day!

V I am a New York Times Bestselling author and by 2020 I have impacted twenty million lives somehow in a positive way.

G.O.A.L.S.V.

(G.O.A. done in the morning and L.S.V. done in the evening):

G   I am so pumped that I get to go to the gym this morning! Today is chest day. gotta get those pecs ready for the beach! #gains

O   Go to South Hill Hospital and follow-up with Nurse Anne on her concern. Secure a commitment to perform a *30* day trial of my product.

A   I can't be stopped. I'm worthy of greatness. I have what it takes. I've put in the work and now it's time to reap the rewards.

L   I learned that price was not Nurse Anne's main concern, it was efficiency. I will adjust my message when I follow-up in a week.

S   It felt so good to volunteer today. The kids loved my message on "Finding Your Passion." I know this approach will help them in their path of discovering not just a job, but a calling.

V   I deeply enjoy being a sought after speaker for Fortune *500* companies and their national sales meetings. I can see the audience; I can feel their energy and reaction to my message.

G. O. A. L. S. V.

DATE

GRATITUDE. OBJECTIVE. AFFIRMATION. LEARN. SERVE. VISUALIZE.

G _____

_____

O _____

_____

A _____

_____

L _____

_____

S _____

_____

V _____

_____

YOU ARE A CHAMPION

G.O.A.L.S. V.

DATE

GRATITUDE. OBJECTIVE. AFFIRMATION. LEARN. SERVE. VISUALIZE.

G _____

_____

O _____

_____

A _____

_____

L _____

_____

S _____

_____

V _____

_____

YOU GOT THIS

G.O.A.L.S. V.

GRATITUDE. OBJECTIVE. AFFIRMATION. LEARN. SERVE. VISUALIZE.

DATE

G _____

_____

O _____

_____

A _____

_____

L _____

_____

S _____

_____

V _____

_____

YOU ARE WORTHY

G.O.A.L.S. V.

DATE

GRATITUDE. OBJECTIVE. AFFIRMATION. LEARN. SERVE. VISUALIZE.

G _____

_____

O _____

_____

A _____

_____

L _____

_____

S _____

_____

V _____

_____

DOMINATE TODAY

G.O.A.L.S. V.

GRATITUDE. OBJECTIVE. AFFIRMATION. LEARN. SERVE. VISUALIZE.

DATE

G _____

_____

O _____

_____

A _____

_____

L _____

_____

S _____

_____

V _____

_____

YOU ARE CHOSEN

G.O.A.L.S. V.

DATE

GRATITUDE. OBJECTIVE. AFFIRMATION. LEARN. SERVE. VISUALIZE.

G _____

_____

O _____

_____

A _____

_____

L _____

_____

S _____

_____

V _____

_____

KEEP CRUSHING IT

G.O.A.L.S. V.

GRATITUDE. OBJECTIVE. AFFIRMATION. LEARN. SERVE. VISUALIZE.

DATE

G _____

_____

O _____

_____

A _____

_____

L _____

_____

S _____

_____

V _____

_____

YOU ARE IN CONTROL OF YOUR THOUGHTS

RISE WEEKLY REFLECTION

Things that made me happy this week:

_____

My key learnings from this week were:

_____

My goal for this week is:

_____

Below is a list of key actions I must do in order to accomplish my weekly goal:

_____

_____

_____

_____

_____

_____

_____

_____

G.O.A.L.S. V.

DATE

GRATITUDE. OBJECTIVE. AFFIRMATION. LEARN. SERVE. VISUALIZE.

G _____

_____

O _____

_____

A _____

_____

L _____

_____

S _____

_____

V _____

_____

YOU ARE IN CONTROL OF YOUR ACTIONS

G _____

_____

O _____

_____

A _____

_____

L _____

_____

S _____

_____

V _____

_____

YOUR HABITS DICTATE YOUR OUTCOMES

G.O.A.L.S. V.

DATE

GRATITUDE. OBJECTIVE. AFFIRMATION. LEARN. SERVE. VISUALIZE.

G _____

O _____

A _____

L _____

S _____

V _____

WITHOUT A GOAL, YOU CAN'T SCORE

G.O.A.L.S. V.

DATE

GRATITUDE. OBJECTIVE. AFFIRMATION. LEARN. SERVE. VISUALIZE.

G _____

_____

O _____

_____

A _____

_____

L _____

_____

S _____

_____

V _____

_____

VICTORY IS IN YOUR EFFORT AND GROWTH, NOTHING ELSE

G.O.A.L.S. V.

DATE

GRATITUDE. OBJECTIVE. AFFIRMATION. LEARN. SERVE. VISUALIZE.

G _____

_____

O _____

_____

A _____

_____

L _____

_____

S _____

_____

V _____

_____

YOU CHOSE YOUR MINDSET – KEEP WORKING AT IT

G.O.A.L.S. V.

DATE

GRATITUDE. OBJECTIVE. AFFIRMATION. LEARN. SERVE. VISUALIZE.

G _____

_____

O _____

_____

A _____

_____

L _____

_____

S _____

_____

V _____

_____

WARRIORS FEEL THE FEAR, BUT GO TO BATTLE ANYWAY

G.O.A.L.S. V.

DATE

GRATITUDE. OBJECTIVE. AFFIRMATION. LEARN. SERVE. VISUALIZE.

G _____

_____

O _____

_____

A _____

_____

L _____

_____

S _____

_____

V _____

_____

YOU HAVE WHAT IT TAKES

RISE WEEKLY REFLECTION

Things that made me happy this week:

_____

My key learnings from this week were:

_____

My goal for this week is:

_____

Below is a list of key actions I must do in order to accomplish my weekly goal:

_____

_____

_____

_____

_____

_____

_____

_____

G.O.A.L.S. V.

DATE

GRATITUDE. OBJECTIVE. AFFIRMATION. LEARN. SERVE. VISUALIZE.

G _____

_____

O _____

_____

A _____

_____

L _____

_____

S _____

_____

V _____

_____

KEEP GOING AND NEVER QUIT

G.O.A.L.S.V.

DATE

GRATITUDE. OBJECTIVE. AFFIRMATION. LEARN. SERVE. VISUALIZE.

G _____

_____

O _____

_____

A _____

_____

L _____

_____

S _____

_____

V _____

_____

YOU ARE LOVED

G.O.A.L.S. V.

DATE

GRATITUDE. OBJECTIVE. AFFIRMATION. LEARN. SERVE. VISUALIZE.

G _____

_____

O _____

_____

A _____

_____

L _____

_____

S _____

_____

V _____

_____

YOUR ACTIONS ARE MAKING A HUGE DIFFERENCE

G.O.A.L.S. V.

DATE

GRATITUDE. OBJECTIVE. AFFIRMATION. LEARN. SERVE. VISUALIZE.

G _____

_____

O _____

_____

A _____

_____

L _____

_____

S _____

_____

V _____

_____

YOU'LL BECOME LUCKIER THE HARDER YOU WORK

G.O.A.L.S. V.

GRATITUDE. OBJECTIVE. AFFIRMATION. LEARN. SERVE. VISUALIZE.

DATE _____

G _____

_____

O _____

_____

A _____

_____

L _____

_____

S _____

_____

V _____

_____

YOU ARE NEVER A FINISHED PRODUCT – KEEP WORKING

G.O.A.L.S.V.

DATE

GRATITUDE. OBJECTIVE. AFFIRMATION. LEARN. SERVE. VISUALIZE.

G _____

_____

O _____

_____

A _____

_____

L _____

_____

S _____

_____

V _____

_____

NOTHING IS GOING TO STOP YOU FROM BEING GREAT

G.O.A.L.S. V.

DATE

GRATITUDE. OBJECTIVE. AFFIRMATION. LEARN. SERVE. VISUALIZE.

G _____

_____

O _____

_____

A _____

_____

L _____

_____

S _____

_____

V _____

_____

YOU ARE A DOMINATING MACHINE

RISE WEEKLY REFLECTION

Things that made me happy this week:

_____

My key learnings from this week were:

_____

My goal for this week is:

_____

Below is a list of key actions I must do in order to accomplish my weekly goal:

_____

_____

_____

_____

_____

_____

_____

_____

G. O. A. L. S. V.

GRATITUDE. OBJECTIVE. AFFIRMATION. LEARN. SERVE. VISUALIZE.

DATE

G _____

_____

O _____

_____

A _____

_____

L _____

_____

S _____

_____

V _____

_____

YOU ARE THE ONLY PERSON IN THE WORLD LIKE YOU

G.O.A.L.S. V.

DATE

GRATITUDE. OBJECTIVE. AFFIRMATION. LEARN. SERVE. VISUALIZE.

G _____

_____

O _____

_____

A _____

_____

L _____

_____

S _____

_____

V _____

_____

YOU HAVE EVERYTHING IT TAKES TO BE THE BEST

G.O.A.L.S. V.

DATE

GRATITUDE. OBJECTIVE. AFFIRMATION. LEARN. SERVE. VISUALIZE.

G _____

_____

O _____

_____

A _____

_____

L _____

_____

S _____

_____

V _____

_____

YOU ARE A BYPRODUCT OF YOUR SELF IMAGE, STANDARDS, & EXPECTATIONS

G.O.A.L.S. V.

DATE

GRATITUDE. OBJECTIVE. AFFIRMATION. LEARN. SERVE. VISUALIZE.

G _____

_____

O _____

_____

A _____

_____

L _____

_____

S _____

_____

V _____

_____

YOU ARE A BLESSING TO THE WORLD

G.O.A.L.S. V.

GRATITUDE. OBJECTIVE. AFFIRMATION. LEARN. SERVE. VISUALIZE.

DATE

G _____

_____

O _____

_____

A _____

_____

L _____

_____

S _____

_____

V _____

_____

WINNERS LIKE TO SEE OTHERS WIN TOO

G.O.A.L.S. V.

DATE

GRATITUDE. OBJECTIVE. AFFIRMATION. LEARN. SERVE. VISUALIZE.

G _____

_____

O _____

_____

A _____

_____

L _____

_____

S _____

_____

V _____

_____

DON'T LET THE MINORITY OR MAJORITY DICTATE YOUR MINDSET

G.O.A.L.S. V.

DATE

GRATITUDE. OBJECTIVE. AFFIRMATION. LEARN. SERVE. VISUALIZE.

G _____

_____

O _____

_____

A _____

_____

L _____

_____

S _____

_____

V _____

_____

GREAT THINGS COME TO THOSE WHO GET OUT OF THEIR COMFORT ZONE

EVEN THE DARKEST NIGHT WILL END AND THE SUN WILL RISE.

VICTOR HUGO, LES MISÉRABLES

RISE MONTHLY RESET

REFLECT ON THE PAST MONTH AND ANSWER THESE QUESTIONS

The accomplishment I am most proud of is:

_____

My biggest key learning from the past month was:

_____

One area I'd like to improve on is:

_____

The mistake that I learned the most from was (favorite failure):

_____

Describe your best day from the past month:

_____

The person or group that I will be more intentional of helping and serving is:

_____

MONTHLY CHALLENGE

PRACTICE SELF CARE - DO SOMETHING NICE FOR YOURSELF THAT RECHARGES YOUR BATTERIES. TREAT YO' SELF! YOU DESERVE IT!

NEW MONTHLY GOAL

MONTH: _____

REASONS WHY THIS IS MY GOAL

ACTIONS I MUST TO DO ACHIEVE MY GOAL	FREQ/DATE

G.O.A.L.S. V.

DATE

GRATITUDE. OBJECTIVE. AFFIRMATION. LEARN. SERVE. VISUALIZE.

G _____

_____

O _____

_____

A _____

_____

L _____

_____

S _____

_____

V _____

_____

YOU ARE A CHAMPION

G.O.A.L.S. V.

DATE

GRATITUDE. OBJECTIVE. AFFIRMATION. LEARN. SERVE. VISUALIZE.

G _____

_____

O _____

_____

A _____

_____

L _____

_____

S _____

_____

V _____

_____

YOU GOT THIS

G.O.A.L.S. V.

DATE

GRATITUDE. OBJECTIVE. AFFIRMATION. LEARN. SERVE. VISUALIZE.

G _____

_____

O _____

_____

A _____

_____

L _____

_____

S _____

_____

V _____

_____

YOU ARE WORTHY

G.O.A.L.S. V.

DATE

GRATITUDE. OBJECTIVE. AFFIRMATION. LEARN. SERVE. VISUALIZE.

G _____

_____

O _____

_____

A _____

_____

L _____

_____

S _____

_____

V _____

_____

DOMINATE TODAY

G.O.A.L.S. V.

DATE

GRATITUDE. OBJECTIVE. AFFIRMATION. LEARN. SERVE. VISUALIZE.

G _____

_____

O _____

_____

A _____

_____

L _____

_____

S _____

_____

V _____

_____

YOU ARE CHOSEN

G.O.A.L.S. V.

DATE

GRATITUDE. OBJECTIVE. AFFIRMATION. LEARN. SERVE. VISUALIZE.

G _____

_____

O _____

_____

A _____

_____

L _____

_____

S _____

_____

V _____

_____

KEEP CRUSHING IT

G.O.A.L.S. V.

DATE

GRATITUDE. OBJECTIVE. AFFIRMATION. LEARN. SERVE. VISUALIZE.

G _____

_____

O _____

_____

A _____

_____

L _____

_____

S _____

_____

V _____

_____

YOU ARE IN CONTROL OF YOUR THOUGHTS

RISE WEEKLY REFLECTION

Things that made me happy this week:

_____

My key learnings from this week were:

_____

My goal for this week is:

_____

Below is a list of key actions I must do in order to accomplish my weekly goal:

_____

_____

_____

_____

_____

_____

_____

G.O.A.L.S. V.

DATE

GRATITUDE. OBJECTIVE. AFFIRMATION. LEARN. SERVE. VISUALIZE.

G _____

_____

O _____

_____

A _____

_____

L _____

_____

S _____

_____

V _____

_____

YOU ARE IN CONTROL OF YOUR ACTIONS

G.O.A.L.S. V.

DATE

GRATITUDE. OBJECTIVE. AFFIRMATION. LEARN. SERVE. VISUALIZE.

G _____

_____

O _____

_____

A _____

_____

L _____

_____

S _____

_____

V _____

_____

YOUR HABITS DICTATE YOUR OUTCOMES

G.O.A.L.S. V.

DATE

GRATITUDE. OBJECTIVE. AFFIRMATION. LEARN. SERVE. VISUALIZE.

G _____

_____

O _____

_____

A _____

_____

L _____

_____

S _____

_____

V _____

_____

WITHOUT A GOAL, YOU CAN'T SCORE

G _____

_____

O _____

_____

A _____

_____

L _____

_____

S _____

_____

V _____

_____

VICTORY IS IN YOUR EFFORT AND GROWTH, NOTHING ELSE

G.O.A.L.S. V.

DATE

GRATITUDE. OBJECTIVE. AFFIRMATION. LEARN. SERVE. VISUALIZE.

G _____

_____

O _____

_____

A _____

_____

L _____

_____

S _____

_____

V _____

_____

YOU CHOSE YOUR MINDSET – KEEP WORKING AT IT

G.O.A.L.S. V.

DATE

GRATITUDE. OBJECTIVE. AFFIRMATION. LEARN. SERVE. VISUALIZE.

G _____

_____

O _____

_____

A _____

_____

L _____

_____

S _____

_____

V _____

_____

WARRIORS FEEL THE FEAR, BUT GO TO BATTLE ANYWAY

G.O.A.L.S. V.

DATE

GRATITUDE. OBJECTIVE. AFFIRMATION. LEARN. SERVE. VISUALIZE.

G _____

_____

O _____

_____

A _____

_____

L _____

_____

S _____

_____

V _____

_____

YOU HAVE WHAT IT TAKES

RISE WEEKLY REFLECTION

Things that made me happy this week:

_____

My key learnings from this week were:

_____

My goal for this week is:

_____

Below is a list of key actions I must do in order to accomplish my weekly goal:

_____

_____

_____

_____

_____

_____

_____

_____

G.O.A.L.S. V.

DATE

GRATITUDE. OBJECTIVE. AFFIRMATION. LEARN. SERVE. VISUALIZE.

G _____

_____

O _____

_____

A _____

_____

L _____

_____

S _____

_____

V _____

_____

KEEP GOING AND NEVER QUIT

G.O.A.L.S. V.

GRATITUDE. OBJECTIVE. AFFIRMATION. LEARN. SERVE. VISUALIZE.

DATE

G _____

_____

O _____

_____

A _____

_____

L _____

_____

S _____

_____

V _____

_____

YOU ARE LOVED

G.O.A.L.S. V.

DATE

GRATITUDE. OBJECTIVE. AFFIRMATION. LEARN. SERVE. VISUALIZE.

G _____

_____

O _____

_____

A _____

_____

L _____

_____

S _____

_____

V _____

_____

YOUR ACTIONS ARE MAKING A HUGE DIFFERENCE

G.O.A.L.S. V.

DATE

GRATITUDE. OBJECTIVE. AFFIRMATION. LEARN. SERVE. VISUALIZE.

G _____

_____

O _____

_____

A _____

_____

L _____

_____

S _____

_____

V _____

_____

YOU'LL BECOME LUCKIER THE HARDER YOU WORK

G . O . A . L . S . V.

DATE

GRATITUDE. OBJECTIVE. AFFIRMATION. LEARN. SERVE. VISUALIZE.

G _____

_____

O _____

_____

A _____

_____

L _____

_____

S _____

_____

V _____

_____

YOU ARE NEVER A FINISHED PRODUCT – KEEP WORKING

G.O.A.L.S. V.

GRATITUDE. OBJECTIVE. AFFIRMATION. LEARN. SERVE. VISUALIZE.

DATE

G _____

_____

O _____

_____

A _____

_____

L _____

_____

S _____

_____

V _____

_____

NOTHING IS GOING TO STOP YOU FROM BEING GREAT

G _____

_____

O _____

_____

A _____

_____

L _____

_____

S _____

_____

V _____

_____

YOU ARE A DOMINATING MACHINE

RISE WEEKLY REFLECTION

Things that made me happy this week:

_____

My key learnings from this week were:

_____

My goal for this week is:

_____

Below is a list of key actions I must do in order to accomplish my weekly goal:

_____

_____

_____

_____

_____

_____

_____

G.O.A.L.S. V.

DATE

GRATITUDE. OBJECTIVE. AFFIRMATION. LEARN. SERVE. VISUALIZE.

G _____

_____

O _____

_____

A _____

_____

L _____

_____

S _____

_____

V _____

_____

YOU ARE THE ONLY PERSON IN THE WORLD LIKE YOU

G. O. A. L. S. V.

GRATITUDE. OBJECTIVE. AFFIRMATION. LEARN. SERVE. VISUALIZE.

G _____

_____

O _____

_____

A _____

_____

L _____

_____

S _____

_____

V _____

_____

YOU HAVE EVERYTHING IT TAKES TO BE THE BEST

G.O.A.L.S. V.

DATE

GRATITUDE. OBJECTIVE. AFFIRMATION. LEARN. SERVE. VISUALIZE.

G _____

_____

O _____

_____

A _____

_____

L _____

_____

S _____

_____

V _____

_____

YOU ARE A BYPRODUCT OF YOUR SELF IMAGE, STANDARDS, & EXPECTATIONS

G . O . A . L . S . V.

DATE

GRATITUDE. OBJECTIVE. AFFIRMATION. LEARN. SERVE. VISUALIZE.

G _____

_____

O _____

_____

A _____

_____

L _____

_____

S _____

_____

V _____

_____

YOU ARE A BLESSING TO THE WORLD

G.O.A.L.S. V.

GRATITUDE. OBJECTIVE. AFFIRMATION. LEARN. SERVE. VISUALIZE.

G _____

_____

O _____

_____

A _____

_____

L _____

_____

S _____

_____

V _____

_____

WINNERS LIKE TO SEE OTHERS WIN TOO

G. O. A. L. S. V.

GRATITUDE. OBJECTIVE. AFFIRMATION. LEARN. SERVE. VISUALIZE.

G _____

_____

O _____

_____

A _____

_____

L _____

_____

S _____

_____

V _____

_____

DON'T LET THE MINORITY OR MAJORITY DICTATE YOUR MINDSET

G.O.A.L.S. V.

GRATITUDE. OBJECTIVE. AFFIRMATION. LEARN. SERVE. VISUALIZE.

G _____

_____

O _____

_____

A _____

_____

L _____

_____

S _____

_____

V _____

_____

GREAT THINGS COME TO THOSE WHO GET OUT OF THEIR COMFORT ZONE

GET THE FUNDAMENTALS DOWN AND THE LEVEL OF EVERYTHING YOU DO WILL RISE.

MICHAEL JORDAN

RISE MONTHLY RESET

REFLECT ON THE PAST MONTH AND ANSWER THESE QUESTIONS

The accomplishment I am most proud of is:

_____

My biggest key learning from the past month was:

_____

One area I'd like to improve on is:

_____

The mistake that I learned the most from was (favorite failure):

_____

Describe your best day from the past month:

_____

The person or group that I will be more intentional of helping and serving is:

_____

MONTHLY CHALLENGE

LISTENING - PRACTICE PUTTING YOUR PHONE AWAY AND MAKE A CONSCIOUS EFFORT TO IMPROVE YOUR LISTENING SKILLS WHILE COMMUNICATING WITH OTHERS.

NEW MONTHLY GOAL

MONTH: _____

REASONS WHY THIS IS MY GOAL

ACTIONS I MUST TO DO ACHIEVE MY GOAL

FREQ/DATE

G.O.A.L.S. V.

DATE

GRATITUDE. OBJECTIVE. AFFIRMATION. LEARN. SERVE. VISUALIZE.

G _____

_____

O _____

_____

A _____

_____

L _____

_____

S _____

_____

V _____

_____

YOU ARE A CHAMPION

G . O . A . L . S . V.

GRATITUDE. OBJECTIVE. AFFIRMATION. LEARN. SERVE. VISUALIZE.

G _____

_____

O _____

_____

A _____

_____

L _____

_____

S _____

_____

V _____

_____

YOU GOT THIS

G.O.A.L.S. V.

GRATITUDE. OBJECTIVE. AFFIRMATION. LEARN. SERVE. VISUALIZE.

G _____

_____

O _____

_____

A _____

_____

L _____

_____

S _____

_____

V _____

_____

YOU ARE WORTHY

G.O.A.L.S. V.

DATE

GRATITUDE. OBJECTIVE. AFFIRMATION. LEARN. SERVE. VISUALIZE.

G _____

_____

O _____

_____

A _____

_____

L _____

_____

S _____

_____

V _____

_____

DOMINATE TODAY

G.O.A.L.S. V.

DATE

GRATITUDE. OBJECTIVE. AFFIRMATION. LEARN. SERVE. VISUALIZE.

G _____

_____

O _____

_____

A _____

_____

L _____

_____

S _____

_____

V _____

_____

YOU ARE CHOSEN

G.O.A.L.S. V.

DATE

GRATITUDE. OBJECTIVE. AFFIRMATION. LEARN. SERVE. VISUALIZE.

G _____

_____

O _____

_____

A _____

_____

L _____

_____

S _____

_____

V _____

_____

KEEP CRUSHING IT

G.O.A.L.S. V.

DATE

GRATITUDE. OBJECTIVE. AFFIRMATION. LEARN. SERVE. VISUALIZE.

G _____

_____

O _____

_____

A _____

_____

L _____

_____

S _____

_____

V _____

_____

YOU ARE IN CONTROL OF YOUR THOUGHTS

RISE WEEKLY REFLECTION

Things that made me happy this week:

_____

My key learnings from this week were:

_____

My goal for this week is:

_____

Below is a list of key actions I must do in order to accomplish my weekly goal:

_____

_____

_____

_____

_____

_____

_____

_____

G.O.A.L.S. V.

GRATITUDE. OBJECTIVE. AFFIRMATION. LEARN. SERVE. VISUALIZE.

G _____

_____

O _____

_____

A _____

_____

L _____

_____

S _____

_____

V _____

_____

YOU ARE IN CONTROL OF YOUR ACTIONS

G.O.A.L.S. V.

DATE

GRATITUDE. OBJECTIVE. AFFIRMATION. LEARN. SERVE. VISUALIZE.

G _____

_____

O _____

_____

A _____

_____

L _____

_____

S _____

_____

V _____

_____

YOUR HABITS DICTATE YOUR OUTCOMES

G.O.A.L.S. V.

DATE

GRATITUDE. OBJECTIVE. AFFIRMATION. LEARN. SERVE. VISUALIZE.

G _____

_____

O _____

_____

A _____

_____

L _____

_____

S _____

_____

V _____

_____

WITHOUT A GOAL, YOU CAN'T SCORE

G.O.A.L.S. V.

DATE

GRATITUDE. OBJECTIVE. AFFIRMATION. LEARN. SERVE. VISUALIZE.

G _____

_____

O _____

_____

A _____

_____

L _____

_____

S _____

_____

V _____

_____

VICTORY IS IN YOUR EFFORT AND GROWTH, NOTHING ELSE

G.O.A.L.S. V.

DATE

GRATITUDE. OBJECTIVE. AFFIRMATION. LEARN. SERVE. VISUALIZE.

G _____

_____

O _____

_____

A _____

_____

L _____

_____

S _____

_____

V _____

_____

YOU CHOSE YOUR MINDSET – KEEP WORKING AT IT

G. O. A. L. S. V.

GRATITUDE. OBJECTIVE. AFFIRMATION. LEARN. SERVE. VISUALIZE.

G _____

_____

O _____

_____

A _____

_____

L _____

_____

S _____

_____

V _____

_____

WARRIORS FEEL THE FEAR, BUT GO TO BATTLE ANYWAY

G.O.A.L.S. V.

DATE

GRATITUDE. OBJECTIVE. AFFIRMATION. LEARN. SERVE. VISUALIZE.

G _____

_____

O _____

_____

A _____

_____

L _____

_____

S _____

_____

V _____

_____

YOU HAVE WHAT IT TAKES

RISE WEEKLY REFLECTION

Things that made me happy this week:

_____

My key learnings from this week were:

_____

My goal for this week is:

_____

Below is a list of key actions I must do in order to accomplish my weekly goal:

_____

_____

_____

_____

_____

_____

_____

_____

G.O.A.L.S. V.

DATE

GRATITUDE. OBJECTIVE. AFFIRMATION. LEARN. SERVE. VISUALIZE.

G _____

_____

O _____

_____

A _____

_____

L _____

_____

S _____

_____

V _____

_____

KEEP GOING AND NEVER QUIT

G.O.A.L.S. V.

DATE

GRATITUDE. OBJECTIVE. AFFIRMATION. LEARN. SERVE. VISUALIZE.

G _____

_____

O _____

_____

A _____

_____

L _____

_____

S _____

_____

V _____

_____

YOU ARE LOVED

G.O.A.L.S. V.

DATE

GRATITUDE. OBJECTIVE. AFFIRMATION. LEARN. SERVE. VISUALIZE.

G _____

_____

O _____

_____

A _____

_____

L _____

_____

S _____

_____

V _____

_____

YOUR ACTIONS ARE MAKING A HUGE DIFFERENCE

G . O . A . L . S . V.

DATE

GRATITUDE. OBJECTIVE. AFFIRMATION. LEARN. SERVE. VISUALIZE.

G _____

_____

O _____

_____

A _____

_____

L _____

_____

S _____

_____

V _____

_____

YOU'LL BECOME LUCKIER THE HARDER YOU WORK

G.O.A.L.S. V.

DATE

GRATITUDE. OBJECTIVE. AFFIRMATION. LEARN. SERVE. VISUALIZE.

G _____

_____

O _____

_____

A _____

_____

L _____

_____

S _____

_____

V _____

_____

YOU ARE NEVER A FINISHED PRODUCT – KEEP WORKING

G. O. A. L. S. V.

DATE

GRATITUDE. OBJECTIVE. AFFIRMATION. LEARN. SERVE. VISUALIZE.

G _____

_____

O _____

_____

A _____

_____

L _____

_____

S _____

_____

V _____

_____

NOTHING IS GOING TO STOP YOU FROM BEING GREAT

G . O . A . L . S . V.

GRATITUDE. OBJECTIVE. AFFIRMATION. LEARN. SERVE. VISUALIZE.

G _____

_____

O _____

_____

A _____

_____

L _____

_____

S _____

_____

V _____

_____

YOU ARE A DOMINATING MACHINE

RISE WEEKLY REFLECTION

Things that made me happy this week:

_____

My key learnings from this week were:

_____

My goal for this week is:

_____

Below is a list of key actions I must do in order to accomplish my weekly goal:

_____

_____

_____

_____

_____

_____

_____

_____

G.O.A.L.S. V.

DATE

GRATITUDE. OBJECTIVE. AFFIRMATION. LEARN. SERVE. VISUALIZE.

G _____

_____

O _____

_____

A _____

_____

L _____

_____

S _____

_____

V _____

_____

YOU ARE THE ONLY PERSON IN THE WORLD LIKE YOU

G.O.A.L.S. V.

DATE

GRATITUDE. OBJECTIVE. AFFIRMATION. LEARN. SERVE. VISUALIZE.

G _____

_____

O _____

_____

A _____

_____

L _____

_____

S _____

_____

V _____

_____

YOU HAVE EVERYTHING IT TAKES TO BE THE BEST

G.O.A.L.S. V.

DATE

GRATITUDE. OBJECTIVE. AFFIRMATION. LEARN. SERVE. VISUALIZE.

G _____

_____

O _____

_____

A _____

_____

L _____

_____

S _____

_____

V _____

_____

YOU ARE A BYPRODUCT OF YOUR SELF IMAGE, STANDARDS, & EXPECTATIONS

G.O.A.L.S. V.

DATE

GRATITUDE. OBJECTIVE. AFFIRMATION. LEARN. SERVE. VISUALIZE.

G _____

_____

O _____

_____

A _____

_____

L _____

_____

S _____

_____

V _____

_____

YOU ARE A BLESSING TO THE WORLD

G.O.A.L.S. V.

DATE

GRATITUDE. OBJECTIVE. AFFIRMATION. LEARN. SERVE. VISUALIZE.

G _____

_____

O _____

_____

A _____

_____

L _____

_____

S _____

_____

V _____

_____

WINNERS LIKE TO SEE OTHERS WIN TOO

G.O.A.L.S. V.

GRATITUDE. OBJECTIVE. AFFIRMATION. LEARN. SERVE. VISUALIZE.

DATE

G _____

_____

O _____

_____

A _____

_____

L _____

_____

S _____

_____

V _____

_____

DON'T LET THE MINORITY OR MAJORITY DICTATE YOUR MINDSET

G.O.A.L.S. V.

DATE

GRATITUDE. OBJECTIVE. AFFIRMATION. LEARN. SERVE. VISUALIZE.

G _____

_____

O _____

_____

A _____

_____

L _____

_____

S _____

_____

V _____

_____

TODAY IS A GREAT DAY TO SMILE AND HELP SOMEONE

WE RISE BY LIFTING OTHERS.

ROBERT INGERSOLL

RISE MONTHLY RESET

REFLECT ON THE PAST MONTH AND ANSWER THESE QUESTIONS

The accomplishment I am most proud of is:

_____

My biggest key learning from the past month was:

_____

One area I'd like to improve on is:

_____

The mistake that I learned the most from was (favorite failure):

_____

Describe your best day from the past month:

_____

The person or group that I will be more intentional of helping and serving is:

_____

MONTHLY CHALLENGE

PERSONAL DEVELOPMENT - WE ARE WHAT WE KNOW.
CONSUME TWO BOOKS THIS MONTH - READ A BOOK
AND LISTEN TO ANOTHER IN AUDIOBOOK FORM.

NEW MONTHLY GOAL

MONTH: _____

REASONS WHY THIS IS MY GOAL

ACTIONS I MUST TO DO ACHIEVE MY GOAL	FREQ/DATE

G.O.A.L.S. V.

DATE

GRATITUDE. OBJECTIVE. AFFIRMATION. LEARN. SERVE. VISUALIZE.

G _____

_____

O _____

_____

A _____

_____

L _____

_____

S _____

_____

V _____

_____

YOU ARE A CHAMPION

G. O. A. L. S. V.

DATE

GRATITUDE. OBJECTIVE. AFFIRMATION. LEARN. SERVE. VISUALIZE.

G _____

_____

O _____

_____

A _____

_____

L _____

_____

S _____

_____

V _____

_____

YOU GOT THIS

G.O.A.L.S. V.

DATE

GRATITUDE. OBJECTIVE. AFFIRMATION. LEARN. SERVE. VISUALIZE.

G _____

_____

O _____

_____

A _____

_____

L _____

_____

S _____

_____

V _____

_____

YOU ARE WORTHY

G.O.A.L.S. V.

GRATITUDE. OBJECTIVE. AFFIRMATION. LEARN. SERVE. VISUALIZE.

DATE

G _____

_____

O _____

_____

A _____

_____

L _____

_____

S _____

_____

V _____

_____

DOMINATE TODAY

G . O . A . L . S . V.

DATE

GRATITUDE. OBJECTIVE. AFFIRMATION. LEARN. SERVE. VISUALIZE.

G _____

_____

O _____

_____

A _____

_____

L _____

_____

S _____

_____

V _____

_____

YOU ARE CHOSEN

G.O.A.L.S. V.

DATE

GRATITUDE. OBJECTIVE. AFFIRMATION. LEARN. SERVE. VISUALIZE.

G _____

_____

O _____

_____

A _____

_____

L _____

_____

S _____

_____

V _____

_____

KEEP CRUSHING IT

G.O.A.L.S. V.

DATE

GRATITUDE. OBJECTIVE. AFFIRMATION. LEARN. SERVE. VISUALIZE.

G _____

_____

O _____

_____

A _____

_____

L _____

_____

S _____

_____

V _____

_____

YOU ARE IN CONTROL OF YOUR THOUGHTS

RISE WEEKLY REFLECTION

Things that made me happy this week:

_____

My key learnings from this week were:

_____

My goal for this week is:

_____

Below is a list of key actions I must do in order to accomplish my weekly goal:

_____

_____

_____

_____

_____

_____

_____

_____

G.O.A.L.S. V.

DATE

GRATITUDE. OBJECTIVE. AFFIRMATION. LEARN. SERVE. VISUALIZE.

G _____

_____

O _____

_____

A _____

_____

L _____

_____

S _____

_____

V _____

_____

YOU ARE IN CONTROL OF YOUR ACTIONS

G.O.A.L.S. V.

DATE

GRATITUDE. OBJECTIVE. AFFIRMATION. LEARN. SERVE. VISUALIZE.

G _____

_____

O _____

_____

A _____

_____

L _____

_____

S _____

_____

V _____

_____

YOUR HABITS DICTATE YOUR OUTCOMES

G.O.A.L.S. V.

DATE

GRATITUDE. OBJECTIVE. AFFIRMATION. LEARN. SERVE. VISUALIZE.

G _____

_____

O _____

_____

A _____

_____

L _____

_____

S _____

_____

V _____

_____

WITHOUT A GOAL, YOU CAN'T SCORE

G.O.A.L.S. V.

GRATITUDE. OBJECTIVE. AFFIRMATION. LEARN. SERVE. VISUALIZE.

DATE _____

G _____

_____

O _____

_____

A _____

_____

L _____

_____

S _____

_____

V _____

_____

VICTORY IS IN YOUR EFFORT AND GROWTH, NOTHING ELSE

G . O . A . L . S . V .

DATE

GRATITUDE. OBJECTIVE. AFFIRMATION. LEARN. SERVE. VISUALIZE.

G _____

_____

O _____

_____

A _____

_____

L _____

_____

S _____

_____

V _____

_____

YOU CHOSE YOUR MINDSET – KEEP WORKING AT IT

G . O . A . L . S . V.

DATE

GRATITUDE. OBJECTIVE. AFFIRMATION. LEARN. SERVE. VISUALIZE.

G _____

_____

O _____

_____

A _____

_____

L _____

_____

S _____

_____

V _____

_____

WARRIORS FEEL THE FEAR, BUT GO TO BATTLE ANYWAY

G.O.A.L.S. V.

DATE

GRATITUDE. OBJECTIVE. AFFIRMATION. LEARN. SERVE. VISUALIZE.

G _____

_____

O _____

_____

A _____

_____

L _____

_____

S _____

_____

V _____

_____

YOU HAVE WHAT IT TAKES

RISE WEEKLY REFLECTION

Things that made me happy this week:

_____

My key learnings from this week were:

_____

My goal for this week is:

_____

Below is a list of key actions I must do in order to accomplish my weekly goal:

_____

_____

_____

_____

_____

_____

_____

_____

G.O.A.L.S. V.

DATE

GRATITUDE. OBJECTIVE. AFFIRMATION. LEARN. SERVE. VISUALIZE.

G _____

_____

O _____

_____

A _____

_____

L _____

_____

S _____

_____

V _____

_____

KEEP GOING AND NEVER QUIT

G.O.A.L.S. V.

DATE

GRATITUDE. OBJECTIVE. AFFIRMATION. LEARN. SERVE. VISUALIZE.

G _____

_____

O _____

_____

A _____

_____

L _____

_____

S _____

_____

V _____

_____

YOU ARE LOVED

G.O.A.L.S. V.

DATE

GRATITUDE. OBJECTIVE. AFFIRMATION. LEARN. SERVE. VISUALIZE.

G _____

_____

O _____

_____

A _____

_____

L _____

_____

S _____

_____

V _____

_____

YOUR ACTIONS ARE MAKING A HUGE DIFFERENCE

G. O. A. L. S. V.

GRATITUDE. OBJECTIVE. AFFIRMATION. LEARN. SERVE. VISUALIZE.

G _____

_____

O _____

_____

A _____

_____

L _____

_____

S _____

_____

V _____

_____

YOU'LL BECOME LUCKIER THE HARDER YOU WORK

G.O.A.L.S. V.

DATE

GRATITUDE. OBJECTIVE. AFFIRMATION. LEARN. SERVE. VISUALIZE.

G _____

_____

O _____

_____

A _____

_____

L _____

_____

S _____

_____

V _____

_____

YOU ARE NEVER A FINISHED PRODUCT – KEEP WORKING

G.O.A.L.S. V.

DATE

GRATITUDE. OBJECTIVE. AFFIRMATION. LEARN. SERVE. VISUALIZE.

G _____

_____

O _____

_____

A _____

_____

L _____

_____

S _____

_____

V _____

_____

NOTHING IS GOING TO STOP YOU FROM BEING GREAT

G.O.A.L.S. V.

DATE

GRATITUDE. OBJECTIVE. AFFIRMATION. LEARN. SERVE. VISUALIZE.

G _____

_____

O _____

_____

A _____

_____

L _____

_____

S _____

_____

V _____

_____

YOU ARE A DOMINATING MACHINE

RISE WEEKLY REFLECTION

Things that made me happy this week:

_____

My key learnings from this week were:

_____

My goal for this week is:

_____

Below is a list of key actions I must do in order to accomplish my weekly goal:

_____

_____

_____

_____

_____

_____

_____

_____

G.O.A.L.S. V.

DATE

GRATITUDE. OBJECTIVE. AFFIRMATION. LEARN. SERVE. VISUALIZE.

G _____

_____

O _____

_____

A _____

_____

L _____

_____

S _____

_____

V _____

_____

YOU ARE THE ONLY PERSON IN THE WORLD LIKE YOU

G.O.A.L.S. V.

DATE

GRATITUDE. OBJECTIVE. AFFIRMATION. LEARN. SERVE. VISUALIZE.

G _____

_____

O _____

_____

A _____

_____

L _____

_____

S _____

_____

V _____

_____

YOU HAVE EVERYTHING IT TAKES TO BE THE BEST

G.O.A.L.S. V.

GRATITUDE. OBJECTIVE. AFFIRMATION. LEARN. SERVE. VISUALIZE.

G _____

_____

O _____

_____

A _____

_____

L _____

_____

S _____

_____

V _____

_____

YOU ARE A BYPRODUCT OF YOUR SELF IMAGE, STANDARDS, & EXPECTATIONS

G . O . A . L . S . V.

DATE

GRATITUDE. OBJECTIVE. AFFIRMATION. LEARN. SERVE. VISUALIZE.

G _____

_____

O _____

_____

A _____

_____

L _____

_____

S _____

_____

V _____

_____

YOU ARE A BLESSING TO THE WORLD

G.O.A.L.S. V.

DATE

GRATITUDE. OBJECTIVE. AFFIRMATION. LEARN. SERVE. VISUALIZE.

G _____

_____

O _____

_____

A _____

_____

L _____

_____

S _____

_____

V _____

_____

WINNERS LIKE TO SEE OTHERS WIN TOO

G.O.A.L.S. V.

GRATITUDE. OBJECTIVE. AFFIRMATION. LEARN. SERVE. VISUALIZE.

G _____

_____

O _____

_____

A _____

_____

L _____

_____

S _____

_____

V _____

_____

DON'T LET THE MINORITY OR MAJORITY DICTATE YOUR MINDSET

G.O.A.L.S. V.

DATE

GRATITUDE. OBJECTIVE. AFFIRMATION. LEARN. SERVE. VISUALIZE.

G _____

_____

O _____

_____

A _____

_____

L _____

_____

S _____

_____

V _____

_____

GREAT THINGS COME TO THOSE WHO GET OUT OF THEIR COMFORT ZONE

OUR GREATEST GLORY IS NOT IN NEVER FALLING, BUT IN RISING EVERY TIME WE FALL.

CONFUCIUS

RISE MONTHLY RESET

REFLECT ON THE PAST MONTH AND ANSWER THESE QUESTIONS

The accomplishment I am most proud of is:

_____

My biggest key learning from the past month was:

_____

One area I'd like to improve on is:

_____

The mistake that I learned the most from was (favorite failure):

_____

Describe your best day from the past month:

_____

The person or group that I will be more intentional of helping and serving is:

_____

MONTHLY CHALLENGE

PRACTICE GRATITUDE – HOW MANY TIMES CAN YOU CALL, TEXT, EMAIL, OR USE SOCIAL MEDIA TO LET SOMEONE KNOW HOW GRATEFUL YOU ARE FOR THEM?

NEW MONTHLY GOAL

MONTH: _____

REASONS WHY THIS IS MY GOAL

ACTIONS I MUST TO DO ACHIEVE MY GOAL	FREQ/DATE

WANT MORE?

THECOLLINHENDERSON.COM